THE ROYAL HORTICULTURAL SOCIETY

WILD IN THE
GARDEN

DIARY
2014

Frances Lincoln Limited
www.franceslincoln.com

The Royal Horticultural Society
Wild in the Garden Diary 2014
Copyright © Frances Lincoln limited 2013
Photographs copyright © individual photographers
as listed in Picture Credits
Text copyright © the Royal Horticultural Society 2013
and printed under licence granted by the Royal Horticultural
Society, Registered Charity number 222879/SC038262.
For more information visit our website or call 0845 130 4646.
An interest in gardening is all you need to enjoy being a member
of the RHS.
Website: www.rhs.org.uk

First Frances Lincoln edition 2013

Astronomical information © Crown Copyright. Reproduced by
permission of the Controller of Her Majesty's Stationery Office
and the UK Hydrographic Office (www.ukho.gov.uk)

A catalogue record for this book is available from
the British Library

ISBN: 978-0-7112-3425-3

Printed in China

1 2 3 4 5 6 7 8 9

Front cover European Hedgehog (*Erinaceus europaeus*)
Back cover Redwing (*Turdus iliacus*) adult, feeding
on European Holly (*Ilex aquifolium*) berries
Introduction Great Tits (*Parus major*)

RHS FLOWER SHOWS 2014

Regrettably Flower Show dates are no longer included in this
diary. Show date changes after publication caused confusion.
The following dates were correct at the time of going to
press but, due to circumstances beyond our control, show
dates often change in the interim period so please confirm
before travelling. Neither the RHS or the publisher can
accept liability for any errors.

CHELSEA FLOWER SHOW (May 20–24 2014), **HAMPTON
COURT PALACE FLOWER SHOW** (July 8–13 2014),
TATTON PARK FLOWER SHOW (July 23–27 2014),
CARDIFF FLOWER SHOW (April 4–6 2014), **MALVERN
FLOWER SHOWS** (May 8–11 and Sept 27–28 2014) and
themed **LONDON SHOWS** throughout the year.

RHS Flower show information

Can be found by visiting www.rhs.org.uk or telephoning the
24-hour Flower Show Information Line (020 7649 1885)

PICTURE CREDITS

All photographs are from The Garden Collection
(www.garden-collection.com)
Paul Hobson/FLPA Front cover, Week 3, Week 41; **Gianpiero
Ferrari/FLPA** Back cover; **Kim Taylor** Introduction, Week
12, Week 16, Week 42; **David Tipling/FLPA** Week 2, Week
5, Week 14; **Mike Powles/FLPA** Week 4; **Paul Sawer/FLPA**
Week 7, Week 35, Week 43; **John Eveson/FLPA** Week 8; **John
Tinning/FLPA** Week 9; **Michael Durham/FLPA** Week 11, Week
13; **Emma Peios** Week 17 (Designed by Nigel Dunnett/RHS
Chelsea 2011); **Mike Lane/FLPA** Week 19; **Bill Coster/FLPA**
Week 20, Week 51, Week 1 2015; **Gerard Lacz/FLPA** Week 21;
Phil McLean/FLPA Week 22, Week 25; **Derek Harris** Week 24
(Designed by Ruth Holmes/RHS Hampton Court 2008), Week
34; **Tony Hamblin/FLPA** Week 26, Week 28; **Michelle Garrett**
Week 29; **Torie Chugg** Week 30 (Jekka's Herb Farm); **Nicola
Stocken Tomkins** Week 31; **Jonathan Buckley** Week 33; **Flora
Press/Stephan Rech** Week 37; **Roger Wilmshurst/FLPA** Week
38, Week 52; **Jane Burton** Week 39; **Derek Middleton/FLPA**
Week 44; **Liz Eddison** Week 46 (Designed by Elaine Hughes/
RHS Hampton Court 2009); **John Watkins/FLPA** Week 47;
Elliott Neep/FLPA Week 48; **Erica Olsen/FLPA** Week 50

CALENDAR 2014

JANUARY
M	T	W	T	F	S	S
		1	2	3	4	5
6	7	8	9	10	11	12
13	14	15	16	17	18	19
20	21	22	23	24	25	26
27	28	29	30	31		

FEBRUARY
M	T	W	T	F	S	S
					1	2
3	4	5	6	7	8	9
10	11	12	13	14	15	16
17	18	19	20	21	22	23
24	25	26	27	28		

MARCH
M	T	W	T	F	S	S
					1	2
3	4	5	6	7	8	9
10	11	12	13	14	15	16
17	18	19	20	21	22	23
24	25	26	27	28	29	30
31						

APRIL
M	T	W	T	F	S	S
	1	2	3	4	5	6
7	8	9	10	11	12	13
14	15	16	17	18	19	20
21	22	23	24	25	26	27
28	29	30				

MAY
M	T	W	T	F	S	S
			1	2	3	4
5	6	7	8	9	10	11
12	13	14	15	16	17	18
19	20	21	22	23	24	25
26	27	28	29	30	31	

JUNE
M	T	W	T	F	S	S
						1
2	3	4	5	6	7	8
9	10	11	12	13	14	15
16	17	18	19	20	21	22
23	24	25	26	27	28	29
30						

JULY
M	T	W	T	F	S	S
	1	2	3	4	5	6
7	8	9	10	11	12	13
14	15	16	17	18	19	20
21	22	23	24	25	26	27
28	29	30	31			

AUGUST
M	T	W	T	F	S	S
				1	2	3
4	5	6	7	8	9	10
11	12	13	14	15	16	17
18	19	20	21	22	23	24
25	26	27	28	29	30	31

SEPTEMBER
M	T	W	T	F	S	S
1	2	3	4	5	6	7
8	9	10	11	12	13	14
15	16	17	18	19	20	21
22	23	24	25	26	27	28
29	30					

OCTOBER
M	T	W	T	F	S	S
		1	2	3	4	5
6	7	8	9	10	11	12
13	14	15	16	17	18	19
20	21	22	23	24	25	26
27	28	29	30	31		

NOVEMBER
M	T	W	T	F	S	S
					1	2
3	4	5	6	7	8	9
10	11	12	13	14	15	16
17	18	19	20	21	22	23
24	25	26	27	28	29	30

DECEMBER
M	T	W	T	F	S	S
1	2	3	4	5	6	7
8	9	10	11	12	13	14
15	16	17	18	19	20	21
22	23	24	25	26	27	28
29	30	31				

CALENDAR 2015

JANUARY
M	T	W	T	F	S	S
			1	2	3	4
5	6	7	8	9	10	11
12	13	14	15	16	17	18
19	20	21	22	23	24	25
26	27	28	29	30	31	

FEBRUARY
M	T	W	T	F	S	S
						1
2	3	4	5	6	7	8
9	10	11	12	13	14	15
16	17	18	19	20	21	22
23	24	25	26	27	28	

MARCH
M	T	W	T	F	S	S
						1
2	3	4	5	6	7	8
9	10	11	12	13	14	15
16	17	18	19	20	21	22
23	24	25	26	27	28	29
30	31					

APRIL
M	T	W	T	F	S	S
		1	2	3	4	5
6	7	8	9	10	11	12
13	14	15	16	17	18	19
20	21	22	23	24	25	26
27	28	29	30			

MAY
M	T	W	T	F	S	S
				1	2	3
4	5	6	7	8	9	10
11	12	13	14	15	16	17
18	19	20	21	22	23	24
25	26	27	28	29	30	31

JUNE
M	T	W	T	F	S	S
1	2	3	4	5	6	7
8	9	10	11	12	13	14
15	16	17	18	19	20	21
22	23	24	25	26	27	28
29	30					

JULY
M	T	W	T	F	S	S
	1	2	3	4	5	
6	7	8	9	10	11	12
13	14	15	16	17	18	19
20	21	22	23	24	25	26
27	28	29	30	31		

AUGUST
M	T	W	T	F	S	S
					1	2
3	4	5	6	7	8	9
10	11	12	13	14	15	16
17	18	19	20	21	22	23
24	25	26	27	28	29	30
31						

SEPTEMBER
M	T	W	T	F	S	S
	1	2	3	4	5	6
7	8	9	10	11	12	13
14	15	16	17	18	19	20
21	22	23	24	25	26	27
28	29	30				

OCTOBER
M	T	W	T	F	S	S
			1	2	3	4
5	6	7	8	9	10	11
12	13	14	15	16	17	18
19	20	21	22	23	24	25
26	27	28	29	30	31	

NOVEMBER
M	T	W	T	F	S	S
						1
2	3	4	5	6	7	8
9	10	11	12	13	14	15
16	17	18	19	20	21	22
23	24	25	26	27	28	29
30						

DECEMBER
M	T	W	T	F	S	S
	1	2	3	4	5	6
7	8	9	10	11	12	13
14	15	16	17	18	19	20
21	22	23	24	25	26	27
28	29	30	31			

GARDENS AND WILDLIFE

Gardens as a network form an important ecosystem. An ecosystem is an interdependent and dynamic system of living organisms which is considered together with the physical and geographical environment. Ecosystems are interdependent because everything in a garden depends on everything else.

The garden ecosystem is extremely variable, thereby offering year-round interest. Gardens can offer a large number of animals the perfect conditions for different stages of their life cycle. Insects may prefer sunny, sheltered spots to forage and mate in, but their larvae may need to live in water or in rotting vegetation. The large range of garden wildlife is there because of gardening, not despite it.

Because of the nature of gardens, groups of species that exploit a network of gardens' resources can find abundance over a longer time period, compared to what a single natural site can offer. Even gardens that are managed without regard for wildlife still offer some benefit, especially when they are considered as part of the total garden network. Even without simulated 'wild' habitats, gardens are living, diverse ecosystems in their own right. No garden is too small to provide some benefit to wildlife. Many visiting animals can actually be residents of neighbouring gardens. It is the garden network that is of overall importance to wildlife, forming the larger garden ecosystem.

City gardens are important corridors that facilitate the safe movement of birds, butterflies and other wildlife. Wildlife-friendly gardens don't need to be messy, with an abundance of stinging nettles. All gardens offer some resource to certain species; however, with a little thought and planning, every garden can be of great benefit to a much wider range of species. Look around your local area and see what type of habitat is missing and whether it is possible for you to provide it: perhaps a pond, nest boxes, decaying wood or an undisturbed leaf pile? The more diverse the habitats that are provided, the greater will be the variety of birds and wildlife visiting your garden.

The RHS recognizes and actively promotes the valuable contribution that gardens make to wildlife, believing that with thoughtful management it is possible to enhance the wildlife potential in any garden without compromising the gardener's enjoyment of it. For more information visit: www.rhs.org.uk and www.wildaboutgardens.org

'Blackbirds, thrushes, tits and robins will be visiting the garden this month'

JOBS FOR THE MONTH
- Hang bird feeders and put out food on the ground and bird table.
- Make sure the bird bath is topped up and the water is not frozen.
- Regularly clean the bird bath and table.
- Make sure the pond does not freeze. Never crack or hit the ice; instead fill a saucepan with hot water and rest it on the ice until a hole has melted.
- Leave out food for hedgehogs (see Week 32).

BIRDS
Winter is the time when birds need your help the most.

Food In the short term you can purchase bird seed, mealworms and fat balls to provide much-needed fat and protein but if you plan ahead you can feed the birds for free (*see Week 18*). Put out food consistently to encourage birds to return regularly.

Water Birds need water to drink and even when it is freezing they love to bathe, so keep containers of water topped up and ice free. Good hygiene is important to prevent the spread of disease, so change the water regularly and clean out bird baths with specialist detergent.

MOTHS
Although perhaps not as instantly appealing as butterflies, moths have an important role to play in the garden. Day moths are plant pollinators and nocturnal moths are a potential food source for bats, nocturnal web-building spiders, owls and small mammals. Moth caterpillars provide food for the young of blue tits, great tits, robins and other birds.
- Plant sea lavender, buddlejas, *Centranthus ruber* and lychnis to attract day-flying moths.
- Plant night-flowering, nectar-rich plants and white or pale-coloured flowering plants to encourage nocturnal moths.
- Plant oak, birch, willow, hawthorn and hornbeam and lady's bedstraw to support moth caterpillars.
- Plant evergreen shrubs to provide winter hibernation sites for butterflies and moths.
- Leave longer grasses, thistles and knapweeds in the garden.

DECEMBER AND JANUARY 2014

Monday 30

New Year's Eve

Tuesday 31

New Moon
New Year's Day
Holiday, UK, Republic of Ireland, USA, Canada,
Australia and New Zealand

Wednesday 1

Holiday, Scotland and New Zealand

Thursday 2

Friday 3

Saturday 4

Sunday 5

JANUARY

---

6 *Monday*   Epiphany

---

7 *Tuesday*

---

8 *Wednesday*   *First Quarter*

---

9 *Thursday*

---

10 *Friday*

---

11 *Saturday*

---

12 *Sunday*

European Blackbird (*Turdus merula*) adult male

JANUARY

Monday 13

Tuesday 14

Wednesday 15

Full Moon

Thursday 16

Friday 17

Saturday 18

Sunday 19

European Hedgehog (*Erinaceus europaeus*) adult

JANUARY

20 *Monday* Holiday, USA (Martin Luther King's Birthday)

21 *Tuesday*

22 *Wednesday*

23 *Thursday*

24 *Friday* Last Quarter

25 *Saturday*

26 *Sunday*

European Robin (*Erithacus rubecula*) adult

JANUARY AND FEBRUARY

Holiday, Australia (Australia Day)   *Monday* 27

Tuesday 28

Wednesday 29

New Moon   *Thursday* 30

Chinese New Year   *Friday* 31

Saturday 1

Sunday 2

Greenfinch (*Carduelis chloris*) and Great Tit (*Parus major*) adults

FEBRUARY

3 *Monday*

4 *Tuesday*

5 *Wednesday*

6 *Thursday*

First Quarter
Accession of Queen Elizabeth II
Holiday, New Zealand (Waitangi Day)

7 *Friday*

8 *Saturday*

9 *Sunday*

'Look out for butterflies such as brimstones and commas, which may emerge during spells of sunshine'

JOBS FOR THE MONTH

- Put up nesting boxes for birds. Choose different types to attract specific birds.
- Keep bird feeders topped up and put food out on the ground and bird table. Avoid foods that could cause choking in young fledglings.
- Keep the bird bath topped up and unfrozen for part of the day.
- Regularly clean the bird bath and table; dispose of old food.
- Make sure the bird bath and table are kept clear of snow.
- Put out hedgehog food (*see* Week 32).
- Keep the pond from freezing over (*see* Week 1).

PREDATORS

Protect birds from predators by siting any bird tables and feeders away from areas easily accessible by cats. Remember cats can easily approach via roofs or trees. Placing feeders next to prickly bushes can be a deterrent. You can give birds warning of a potential predator by attaching multiple bells to your cat's collar.

VARIED HABITATS

The best way to encourage a variety of wildlife into your garden is to provide a range of different habitats.

Ponds Even the smallest pond will attract dragonflies, damselflies and other insects, as well as newts, toads and frogs. A pond also provides an important water source for all wildlife.

Logs Logs are a perfect habitat for insects as well as providing potential hibernation places for small mammals and amphibians and nesting sites for some birds. All of these creatures are part of the food chain. Retaining an old tree with cavities or splits in the trunk, or even just leaving a log or two in a corner, will benefit wildlife.

Hedges Hedges provide important corridors for wildlife to move along safely, as well as protection from the elements, nesting and hibernation sites, and food. Replace a fence or exotic hedge with a native hedgerow of hawthorn (*Crataegus monogyna*), blackthorn (*Prunus spinosa*), field maple (*Acer campestre*) or hazel (*Corylus avellana*).

Compost heaps Insects, which are an important food source, live in compost heaps.

FEBRUARY

Monday 10

Tuesday 11

1200 - 1800 Gas boiler - annual service

Wednesday 12

Thursday 13

Full Moon
Valentine's Day

Friday 14

Saturday 15

Sunday 16

Blue Tit (*Parus caeruleus*) adult

FEBRUARY

17 *Monday*

Holiday, USA (Washington's Birthday)

18 *Tuesday*

19 *Wednesday*

20 *Thursday*

21 *Friday*

22 *Saturday*

Last Quarter

23 *Sunday*

Eastern Grey Squirrel (*Sciurus carolinensis*) adult

FEBRUARY AND MARCH

Monday 24

Tuesday 25

Wednesday 26

Thursday 27

Friday 28

New Moon
St David's Day

Saturday 1

Sunday 2

Goldfinch (*Carduelis carduelis*) adult

MARCH

---

3 *Monday*

---

4 *Tuesday*   Shrove Tuesday

- Allan Luke, here, 13:00

---

5 *Wednesday*   Ash Wednesday

---

6 *Thursday*

---

7 *Friday*

---

8 *Saturday*   First Quarter

---

9 *Sunday*

Look for amphibian spawn in ponds. Frog spawn is usually in jelly-like clumps; toad spawn is in long double strands; newt spawn is laid individually on pondweed stems.

'Look out for birds gathering materials for nest building'

BIRD FEEDERS

- Use wire-mesh feeders for peanuts (but avoid putting these out until fledglings are old enough not to choke on them).
- Niger seeds, which are favourites of goldfinches, need a specially designed feeder.
- Encourage ground-feeding birds such as robins and dunnocks by placing food on wire mesh positioned just off the ground.
- Use wire cages rather than plastic nets for fat blocks, as the latter can be dangerous for some birds.
- Create your own fat blocks by melting suet into moulds such as coconut shells or logs with holes drilled into them.
- Clean feeders regularly and move them around the garden to avoid fouling the ground underneath.
- Water containers should be shallow, preferably with sloping sides and no more than 5cm (2in) deep.
- Put out different types of bird food to attract individual species (*see* Week 23).

JOBS FOR THE MONTH

- Put up nesting boxes for birds.
- Top up bird feeders and put food out on the ground and bird table.
- Avoid chunky foods, such as peanuts, that might cause young fledglings to choke.
- Keep the bird bath topped up and clean it regularly.
- Put out hedgehog food (*see* Week 32).
- Make your pond more wildlife friendly (*see* Week 45).
- Sow or plant a wildflower meadow.
- Hang a bat nesting box.
- Create log and twig piles from prunings and felled trees. This will provide protection and debris for nests, and shelter for small mammals and some birds.
- Remove any netting placed over the pond to protect it from autumn leaf fall.

MARCH

Commonwealth Day

Monday 10

Tuesday 11

Wednesday 12

Thursday 13

Friday 14

Saturday 15

Full Moon

Sunday 16

Common Frog (*Rana temporaria*) adult

MARCH

---

17 *Monday*

St Patrick's Day
Holiday, Northern Ireland and Republic of Ireland

---

18 *Tuesday*

---

19 *Wednesday*

---

20 *Thursday*

Vernal Equinox (Spring begins)

---

21 *Friday*

---

22 *Saturday*

---

23 *Sunday*

Brown Hawker Dragonfly (*Aeshna grandis*) male

MARCH

Last Quarter

Monday 24

Tuesday 25

Wednesday 26

Thursday 27

Friday 28

Saturday 29

Sunday 30

New Moon
British Summer Time begins
Mother's Day, UK and Republic of Ireland

Long-tailed Tit (*Aegithalos caudatus*) adult, collecting nesting material

MARCH AND APRIL

31 *Monday*

1 *Tuesday*

2 *Wednesday*

3 *Thursday*

4 *Friday*

5 *Saturday*

6 *Sunday*

Great Tit (*Parus major*) adult, feeding chick

'Look out for migrant birds such as willow warblers, housemartins, swifts and swallows arriving from Africa'

JOBS FOR THE MONTH

- Put up nesting boxes for birds.
- Top up bird feeders and put food out on the ground and bird table (*see* Week 10 and Week 23).
- Avoid chunky foods that might cause young fledglings to choke.
- Keep the bird bath topped up.
- Put out hedgehog food (*see* Week 32).
- Make your pond more wildlife friendly (*see* Week 45).
- Create log, twig and/or rock piles to provide shelter for wildlife.
- Plant annuals and perennials to attract insects.
- Plant single flowers to encourage beneficial insects into the garden.

BATS

Bats begin roosting now. Many bat species eat midges and tiny insects, so encourage bats into your garden by making it more bat friendly. Avoid using pesticides where possible. Look at available habitats; ponds and compost heaps are favoured by insects that bats like to eat. Grow plants to attract moths and other night-flying insects (*see* Week 1). Be insect tolerant – caterpillars will give a bat a meal.

BEES

Bees are important pollinators in the garden and they are becoming increasingly vulnerable, partly because of loss of habitat. Make some changes to support and encourage the many different species in Britain:

- Provide them with flowers from February to November.
- Plant clumps of bee-friendly plants in sunny places.
- Avoid double or multi-petalled cultivars of plants.
- Use pesticides sparingly – particularly spraying open flowers. If you have to spray, spray in the evening when bees are less active.
- Create nest sites for solitary bees in sunny spots with hollow stems (bamboo canes or herbaceous plant stems), cardboard tubes, which can be purchased, or holes (2–8mm deep) can be drilled into fence posts.

APRIL

First Quarter

Monday 7

Tuesday 8

Wednesday 9

Thursday 10

Friday 11

Saturday 12

Palm Sunday

Sunday 13

APRIL

---

14 *Monday*

---

15 *Tuesday*

Full Moon
First day of Passover (Pesach)

---

16 *Wednesday*

---

17 *Thursday*

Maundy Thursday

---

18 *Friday*

Good Friday
Holiday, UK, Canada,
Australia and New Zealand

---

19 *Saturday*

Holiday, Australia (Easter Saturday)

---

20 *Sunday*

Easter Sunday

European Starling (*Sturnus vulgaris*) visiting nest box with fledged chicks

APRIL

Easter Monday
Holiday, UK (exc. Scotland), Republic of Ireland,
Australia and New Zealand
Birthday of Queen Elizabeth II

Monday 21

Last Quarter

Tuesday 22

St George's Day

Wednesday 23

Thursday 24

Holiday, Australia and New Zealand (Anzac Day)

Friday 25

Saturday 26

Sunday 27

A dry stone wall creates habitats for insects

28 *Monday*

29 *Tuesday*   *New Moon*

30 *Wednesday*

1 *Thursday*

2 *Friday*

3 *Saturday*

~ 10 00 Gardening, Longtown Road, Brampton
1 hour worked, £10 received

4 *Sunday*

'Bug life is thriving. Damselflies and dragonflies are attracted to ponds. Pond skaters and water boatmen can be found on pond surfaces'

JOBS FOR THE MONTH
- Put up nesting boxes.
- Avoid disturbing nesting birds in garden shrubs and hedges.
- Top up bird feeders and put food out on the ground and bird table. Avoid chunky foods that might cause young fledglings to choke (*see* Week 10 and right).
- Regularly top up and clean out the bird bath and table.
- Make your pond more wildlife friendly (*see* Week 45).
- Remove weeds from ponds, leaving them on the side for twenty-four hours to allow trapped creatures to return to the water before adding them to the compost heap.
- Create log, twig and/or rock piles to create shelter for wildlife.
- Choose annuals and perennials to attract insects.
- Leave informal hedges un-trimmed for a while to provide food and shelter for wildlife.

BIRDS
Look out for nesting birds in garden shrubs and hedges.

CREATE YOUR OWN BIRD FOOD
Bird food need not be shop bought or expensive.
- Create your own fat blocks for birds by melting suet into moulds such as coconut shells.
- Plant your own 'bird café' including teasels, sunflowers, cardoons and other thistle flowers, as well as berrying shrubs like cotoneaster, blackthorn or pyracantha. This habitat will also encourage insects such as spiders who are pest controllers as well as part of the food chain.
- When autumn comes leave windfalls on the ground and seed heads and hips on the plant to create a free food source for birds.

MAY

Early Spring Bank Holiday, UK
Holiday, Republic of Ireland
Holiday, Australia (Labour Day)

Monday 5

Tuesday 6

First Quarter

Wednesday 7

Thursday 8

Friday 9

Saturday 10

Sunday 11

Mother's Day, USA, Canada,
Australia and New Zealand

European Goldfinch (*Carduelis carduelis*) adult

MAY

12 *Monday*

13 *Tuesday*

14 *Wednesday*   *Full Moon*

15 *Thursday*

16 *Friday*

17 *Saturday*

18 *Sunday*

MAY

Holiday, Canada (Victoria Day)

10:00 Dentist - cancelled

Last Quarter

---

10 00 Gardening, Longtown Road, Brampton
take secateurs (gloves, kneeler ...)
1 hour worked, £10 received

European Red Fox (*Vulpes vulpes*) young cub

26 *Monday*

Spring Bank Holiday, UK
Holiday, USA (Memorial Day)

27 *Tuesday*

28 *Wednesday*

New Moon

29 *Thursday*

Ascension Day

30 *Friday*

31 *Saturday*

1 *Sunday*

Small White (*Artogela rapae*) adult on Nasturtium, a larval food plant

'Hedgehog litters are being born and may come out to forage at night'

MAMMALS & AMPHIBIANS

Hedgehog litters are being born. You may see or hear their parents foraging for food at night. Tadpoles are developing the adult 'frog-legs'. They are emerging from the water to seek shelter among marginal pond plantings and are now vulnerable to predators.

JOBS FOR THE MONTH

- Continue to put out food for birds on a regular basis, avoiding chunky foods that might cause young fledglings to choke (*see* Week 10 and Week 18).
- Consider having a bird bath, as it can be a vital source of drinking water for birds. Birds also like to bathe all year. Always clean it regularly and keep it topped up.
- Build a 'ladybird hotel' using bundles of hollow stems or twigs.
- Put up a bat nesting box.
- Put out hedgehog food (see Week 32).
- Thin out, cut back or divide excessive new growth on aquatic plants.
- Create log, twig and/or rock piles to provide shelter for small mammals and insects.
- Use wildlife-friendly slug pellets.
- Mow spring-flowering meadows once bulb foliage has died down.
- Control weeds by mowing recently established perennial meadows.

CHOOSING BIRD FOOD

Provide birds with a balanced diet of grain mix and nuts as well as fat. Use different foods to entice particular birds to your garden:

- **Tits** like insect cakes
- **Finches** like berry cakes
- **Wrens and small birds** eat finely chopped animal fat and grated cheese
- **Sparrows, finches and nuthatches** like sunflower heads
- **Goldfinches** eat niger seeds
- **Starlings** like peanut cakes
- **Thrushes and blackbirds** eat fruit. Scatter over-ripe apples, raisins and song-bird mixes on the ground. Plant berrying shrubs and trees such as malus, sorbus, cotoneaster and pyracantha.

IN THE GARDEN

Avoid pruning hip-producing roses. The hips are a useful source of food for wildlife.

JUNE

Coronation Day
Holiday, Republic of Ireland
Holiday, New Zealand (The Queen's Birthday)

Monday 2

Tuesday 3

Feast of Weeks (Shavuot)

Wednesday 4

First Quarter

Thursday 5

Friday 6

Saturday 7

Whit Sunday

Sunday 8

JUNE

---

9 *Monday*

---

10 *Tuesday*

---

11 *Wednesday*

---

12 *Thursday*

---

13 *Friday*

Full Moon

---

14 *Saturday*

The Queen's Official Birthday,
subject to confirmation

10 00 Gardening, Longtown Road, Brampton
take secateurs (gloves, kneeler ...)
1 hour worked, £10 received

---

15 *Sunday*

Trinity Sunday
Father's Day, UK, Republic of Ireland,
USA and Canada

Wildlife and recycled garden

JUNE

Monday 16

Tuesday 17

Wednesday 18

Last Quarter
Corpus Christi

Thursday 19

Friday 20

Summer Solstice (Summer begins)

Saturday 21

Sunday 22

Greater Spotted Woodpecker (*Dendrocopus major*) adult male

JUNE

23 *Monday*

24 *Tuesday*

25 *Wednesday*

26 *Thursday*

27 *Friday*   *New Moon*

28 *Saturday*

29 *Sunday*   *First day of Ramadân*

Seven-spot Ladybird *(Coccinella septempunctata)* adult

'This is prime time for bat watching'

JOBS FOR THE MONTH

- Top up bird feeders and put food out on the ground and bird tables (*see* Week 10 and Week 18).
- Avoid chunky foods that might cause young fledglings to choke.
- Keep the bird bath topped up and clean regularly.
- Plant marigolds around the vegetable patch to attract hoverflies for pest control.
- Put out hedgehog food (*see* Week 32).
- Construct a hedgehog hibernation box for the coming winter.
- Plant annuals and perennials to attract insects.
- Trim hedges less frequently to allow wildlife to shelter and feed in them.
- Leave nesting birds undisturbed in garden shrubs and trees.
- Avoid deadheading roses that produce hips, as these are a valuable food source.
- Top up ponds and water features if necessary. Aerating the water using a hose with spray attachment adds oxygen, which will help the fish.
- Remove dead foliage and blooms from aquatic plants.

MAMMALS & AMPHIBIANS

Young mammals are venturing out of the nest. Young litters of hedgehogs are now learning how to survive and may be seen foraging at night. Adult frogs, toads and newts start leaving the pond when the ground is damp. Look out for bats, which are around at this time of year. If you have put up a bat box, be patient, as it can take years for it to be inhabited. Look for droppings or other signs of use.

SPIDERS

Spiders have an important role to play in the garden. As well as eating insects, they are part of the food chain and are a food source for birds.

- Plant tall plants and dense bushes to create scaffolding for spiders to build their webs on.
- Cover bare soil with mulch. This keeps soil moist and provides a home for insects, a food source for spiders.
- Use pesticides as little as possible and if you have to spray, do it in the evening.

INSECTS

Harmless hoverflies are in abundance. They are good garden pest catchers. Wasps are also good pest controllers, eating flies and grubs. They are also useful flower pollinators.

JUNE AND JULY

Monday 30

Holiday, Canada (Canada Day)   *Tuesday* 1

Wednesday 2

Thursday 3

Holiday, USA (Independence Day)   *Friday* 4

First Quarter   *Saturday* 5

Sunday 6

JULY

---

7 *Monday*

---

8 *Tuesday*

---

9 *Wednesday*

---

10 *Thursday*

---

11 *Friday*

---

12 *Saturday*

Full Moon
Battle of the Boyne

---

13 *Sunday*

Dunnock (*Prunella modularis*) adult

Holiday, Northern Ireland (Battle of the Boyne) — *Monday* 14

St Swithin's Day — *Tuesday* 15

11 40   Dentist

Wednesday 16

Thursday 17

Friday 18

Last Quarter — *Saturday* 19

10 00   Gardening, Longtown Road, Brampton
        take secateurs (gloves, kneeler...) - postponed

'STHS meal', evening — *Sunday* 20

1500 Gardening - see 19 July - 1 hour worked,
      £10 received

Helenium and Hoverfly

JULY

21 *Monday*

22 *Tuesday*

23 *Wednesday*

24 *Thursday*

25 *Friday*

26 *Saturday*   *New Moon*

27 *Sunday*

Comma (*Polygonia c-album*) Butterfly on *Ammi visnaga*

JULY AND AUGUST

Eid al-Fitr (end of Ramadân)

Monday 28

Tuesday 29

Wednesday 30

Thursday 31

Friday 1

Saturday 2

Sunday 3

Small informal wildlife pond with water lilies and edged with a pebble beach

AUGUST

4 *Monday*

5 *Tuesday*

6 *Wednesday*

7 *Thursday*

8 *Friday*

9 *Saturday*

10 *Sunday*

Full Moon

'Young birds may be seen exploring their environment'

MAMMALS & AMPHIBIANS

Young frogs and newts start to leave the ponds where they were born to move further afield.

BIRDS

Many adult birds fly fairly low in late summer, hiding in cool, shady places while their feathers change in the summer moult. Birdsong may be reduced this month. New young birds may be seen exploring their environment. In hot, dry weather many birds enjoy 'dust-bathing' as well as splashing about in the bird bath or pond.

JOBS FOR THE MONTH

- Top up bird feeders and put food out on the ground and bird tables.
- Avoid chunky foods that might cause young fledglings to choke (*see* Week 10 and Week 18).
- Keep the bird bath topped up.
- Clean bird baths and tables regularly.
- Plant marigolds around the vegetable patch for pest control.
- Put out hedgehog food (*see* right).
- Construct a hedgehog hibernation box.
- Plant annuals and perennials to attract insects.
- Trim hedges less frequently to allow wildlife to shelter and feed in them.
- Leave nesting birds undisturbed in garden shrubs and trees.
- Allow seed heads to develop on some plants as a food source.

HEDGEHOGS

Hedgehogs eat snails, slugs, beetles, caterpillars and worms. You can supplement their food in winter by feeding them dog or cat food but avoid bread and milk. They like to wander, so providing safe 'corridors' such as hedges will offer them some protection. They prefer a habitat of thick dense undergrowth and varying lengths of grass, and like to hibernate in leaf piles, in compost heaps or under hedges or sheds. You can build or buy them a hibernation box quite easily.

AUGUST

Monday 11

Tuesday 12

Wednesday 13

Thursday 14

Friday 15

Saturday 16

Last Quarter

Sunday 17

Poached Egg Plant (*Limnanthes douglasii*), attractive to bees

AUGUST

18 *Monday*

19 *Tuesday*

20 *Wednesday*

21 *Thursday*

22 *Friday*

23 *Saturday*

24 *Sunday*

AUGUST

Monday 25

Tuesday 26

Wednesday 27

Thursday 28

Friday 29

Saturday 30

10 00   Gardening, Longtown Road, Brampton
         take secateurs, gloves, kneeler...
         1 hour worked, £10 received

Sunday 31

Blue Tit (*Parus caeruleus*) adult, foraging on Bramble (*Rubus fruticosus*) berries

SEPTEMBER

1 *Monday*

2 *Tuesday*

11 30 Dentist

3 *Wednesday*

4 *Thursday*

5 *Friday*

6 *Saturday*

7 *Sunday*

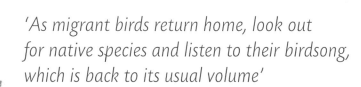

'As migrant birds return home, look out for native species and listen to their birdsong, which is back to its usual volume'

JOBS FOR THE MONTH

- Continue to feed birds, avoiding chunky foods that might cause young fledglings to choke (*see* Week 10 and Week 18).
- Keep the bird bath topped up and clean regularly.
- Put out hedgehog food (*see* Week 32).
- Construct a hedgehog hibernation box.
- Trim hedges less frequently to create shelter for wildlife.
- Give meadows a final cut before winter.
- Cover the pond surface with netting to stop fallen leaves from entering.

PREPARE FOR WINTER

Help hibernating creatures survive the cold weather by making hibernation places in your garden:

- Create a log pile for beetles.
- Make a 'ladybird hotel' out of hollow stems.
- Build a hedgehog box.
- Leave a pile of old leaves undisturbed to provide a home for small mammals and many insects.

IN THE GARDEN

Save yourself some work and help wildlife at the same time:

- Leave windfalls on the ground Blackbirds, thrushes and fieldfares will love them.
- Leave informal hedges untrimmed to provide food and shelter for wildlife.
- Restrain yourself from deadheading hip-producing roses, as they are an important food source.
- Leave prunings and garden debris in a pile to provide shelter for small wildlife such as hedgehogs as well as debris for nest building.
- Leave herbaceous and hollow stemmed plants unpruned, as these can provide homes for overwintering insects.
- Leave mature ivy uncut to flower. It provides an excellent late nectar food source for insects.
- Leave meadow clippings to lie for a couple of days before removing to allow wildlife to crawl back into the sward.

SEPTEMBER

Monday 8

Full Moon

Tuesday 9

Wednesday 10

Thursday 11

Friday 12

Saturday 13

Sunday 14

Eurasian Red Squirrel (*Sciurus vulgaris*) adult

SEPTEMBER

15 *Monday*

16 *Tuesday*

17 *Wednesday*

14:00   Hous; planning group for lay led services

18 *Thursday*

19 *Friday*

20 *Saturday*

21 *Sunday*

Redwing (*Turdus iliacus*) on Cotoneaster

SEPTEMBER

Monday 22

Autumnal Equinox (Autumn begins)

Tuesday 23

Wednesday 24

Jewish New Year (Rosh Hashanah)

Thursday 25

Friday 26

Saturday 27

Sunday 28

Young Oak (*Quercus robur*) leaves with Speckled Bush Cricket (*Leptophyes punctatissima*)

SEPTEMBER AND OCTOBER

29 *Monday* Michaelmas Day

30 *Tuesday*

1 *Wednesday* First Quarter

2 *Thursday*

3 *Friday*

4 *Saturday* Day of Atonement (Yom Kippur)

10 00 Gardening, Longtown Road, Brampton
take secateurs, gloves, kneeler... cancelled -
rain

5 *Sunday*

'Holly blue butterfly larvae can be seen as little caterpillars feeding on ivy.'

JOBS FOR THE MONTH

- Top up bird feeders and put food out on the ground and bird tables. All feeds, including peanuts, are safe, as the breeding season is now over (*see* Week 10 and Week 18).
- Keep the bird bath topped up and clean regularly.
- Put out hedgehog food (*see* Week 32).
- Construct a hedgehog hibernation box.
- Where possible leave seed heads standing to provide food and shelter for wildlife. If possible leave mature ivy uncut to flower.
- Make a leaf pile for hibernating mammals and overwintering ground-feeding birds; add in some logs to widen the appeal for a greater range of insects; or build a 'bug hotel'.

BIRDS

Winter migrants start to arrive from colder, northern regions. Geese and ducks can be arriving in droves. In the garden you may spot redwings, bramblings and fieldfares.

MAMMALS

Mammals start going into hibernation. Be careful when turning compost heaps, as frogs, toads and small animals often shelter there. As food sources become scarce foxes may become nocturnal pests, so always secure your rubbish.

INSECTS

- Leaving herbaceous and hollow stemmed plants unpruned until early spring will provide homes for over-wintering insects.
- Many butterflies, including tortoiseshells, are still about, along with hoverflies and ladybirds. Autumn daisies are important for butterflies and bees as there are fewer other plants in flower for them to feed on. Mature ivy flowers late, providing an excellent nectar source for wildlife.
- Although emerging caterpillars eat your plants they will grow into butterflies that will help with pollination (and will look beautiful too). Top favourite food for caterpillars includes stinging nettle, thistle, wild carrot, bird's-foot trefoil, buckthorn and blackthorn.

OCTOBER

Monday 6

Tuesday 7

Full Moon

Wednesday 8

First Day of Tabernacles (Succoth)

Thursday 9

Friday 10

Saturday 11

Sunday 12

Short-eared Owl (*Asio flammeus*) adult

OCTOBER

---

13 *Monday*

19 30 Stonechats, Hayton - meeting to plan
          for Armistice Day commemoration

---

14 *Tuesday*

---

15 *Wednesday*

Last Quarter

---

16 *Thursday*

---

17 *Friday*

09 00 at How: planning group for lay lech
          services

---

18 *Saturday*

10 00 Gardening, Longtown Road, Brampton
          (see 4 October); 1 hour worked,
          £10 received

---

19 *Sunday*

Marbled White Butterfly (*Melanargia galathea*) on Field Scabious (*Knautia arvensis*)

OCTOBER

Monday 20

Tuesday 21

Wednesday 22

New Moon

Thursday 23

Friday 24

Islamic New Year

Saturday 25

British Summer Time ends

Sunday 26

Great Tit (*Parus major*) adult

27 *Monday*

Holiday, Republic of Ireland
Holiday, New Zealand (Labour Day)

28 *Tuesday*

29 *Wednesday*

30 *Thursday*

31 *Friday*

First Quarter
Halloween

1 *Saturday*

All Saints' Day

2 *Sunday*

Field Vole (*Microtus agrestis*) adult

'Greenfinches, chaffinches and sparrows will all be visiting the birdfeeder'

DESIGNING A POND

Having a pond in the garden is the quickest way to encourage a variety of wildlife into your garden. Within a short period of time a pond will attract birds, amphibians, insects, mammals and a whole range of mini-beasts. If you build your pond in the winter the first toads may arrive in the spring. Amphibians eat slugs, so your garden plants will benefit too.

- Choose a sunny site.
- Conserve water and connect your water butt so that it fills the pond automatically during heavy rain.
- Ensure at least one side of the pond is sloping to provide easy access in and out of the water.
- Make sure there is sufficient space around the edge for dense waterside planting, as this can provide a safe 'corridor' to hibernation areas.
- Avoid using cobbles and paving around the edges, as these surfaces heat up fast in the sun and can be lethal for young amphibians crossing to reach shady areas.
- Create a nearby log pile using the biggest logs you can find. All kinds of insects will love it.
- To encourage newts to breed, introduce some non-invasive submerged aquatic plants into the pond. Newts lay their eggs on narrow-leaved plants.
- Place rocks or logs in the pond but protruding above the waterline to provide places where frogs and toads can rest and breathe above the water.

JOBS FOR THE MONTH

- All bird feeds are now safe, so continue to put food out regularly.
- Keep the bird bath topped up and clean regularly.
- Make a hedgehog hibernation box.
- Leave seed heads standing to provide food and shelter for wildlife.
- Leave mature ivy uncut to flower. The nectar is a food source for insects.
- Make a leaf pile for hibernating mammals and overwintering ground-feeding birds.
- Empty and clean out nesting boxes with boiling water. When thoroughly dry, place a handful of wood shavings inside. They may provide winter shelter. It is illegal to remove unhatched eggs except between November and January.
- Regularly shake off leaves from nets over ponds. Rake out leaves from ponds that are not netted.

NOVEMBER

Monday 3

Tuesday 4

Guy Fawkes

Wednesday 5

Full Moon

Thursday 6

Friday 7

Saturday 8

Remembrance Sunday

Sunday 9

NOVEMBER

10 *Monday*

11 *Tuesday*

Holiday, USA (Veterans Day
Holiday, Canada (Remembrance Day

12 *Wednesday*

13 *Thursday*

14 *Friday*

Last Quarter

15 *Saturday*

16 *Sunday*

Log pile and compost bin in a wildlife garden

NOVEMBER

Monday 17

Tuesday 18

Wednesday 19

Thursday 20

Friday 21

New Moon

Saturday 22

Sunday 23

Blue Tit (*Parus caeruleus*)

NOVEMBER

24 *Monday*

25 *Tuesday*

26 *Wednesday*

27 *Thursday*

Holiday, USA (Thanksgiving Day)

28 *Friday*

29 *Saturday*

First Quarter

30 *Sunday*

St Andrew's Day
First Sunday in Advent

Wood Mouse (*Apodemus sylvaticus*) young, foraging in leaf litter

'Listen out for the male robin marking out his territory through song'

JOBS FOR THE MONTH
- Top up bird feeders and put food out on the ground and bird tables (*see* Week 10 and Week 18). Once a feeding regime is established try and keep to it, as this will encourage birds to return.
- All bird feed, including peanuts, are safe, as the breeding season is over.
- Keep the bird bath topped up and ice free (*see* Week 1).
- Clean bird baths and tables regularly.
- Where possible leave seed heads standing to provide food and shelter for wildlife.
- If possible leave mature ivy uncut to flower.
- Make a leaf pile for hibernating mammals and over wintering ground-feeding birds.

INSECTS
Butterflies and moths hibernate through the winter in places that are sheltered from wind, frost and rain. They prefer a habitat of evergreen plants and thick tangles of leaves and stems, so either plant shrubs to encourage them or give yourself a break from pruning.

PLANT FOR WILDLIFE
- Planting a single tree provides a host of habitats for a wide variety of insects and mammals. Native trees will always support more wildlife than imported varieties.
- Consider planting more shrubs and trees that produce berries in order to provide a valuable food source for garden birds. Red and orange berries are reported to be more popular with birds than yellow berries.
- Holly (*Ilex*) is a traditional part of Christmas; however, holly berries are a valuable source of food for birds, so don't take them all for Christmas! In spring Holly Blue butterfly larvae feed on holly flower buds and berries.
- Native ivy is also very good for wildlife. The flowers feed bees, butterflies and hoverflies, and the thick tangle of stems and leaves make winter homes for many butterflies and other insects. The birds eat the berries too.

DECEMBER

Monday 1

Tuesday 2

Wednesday 3

Thursday 4

Friday 5

Saturday 6

Full Moon

Sunday 7

DECEMBER

8 *Monday*

9 *Tuesday*

10 *Wednesday*

11 *Thursday*

12 *Friday*

13 *Saturday*

14 *Sunday*

Last Quarter

Chaffinch (*Fringilla coelebs*) adult male

DECEMBER

Monday 15

Tuesday 16

Hannukah begins

Wednesday 17

Thursday 18

Friday 19

Saturday 20

Sunday 21

Winter Solstice (Winter begins)

European Blackbird (*Turdus merula*) adult male

DECEMBER

22 *Monday*   *New Moo*

23 *Tuesday*

24 *Wednesday*   Christmas Ev
                                                            Hannukah end

25 *Thursday*   Christmas Day
                                        Holiday, UK, Republic of Ireland, USA, Canada
                                                      Australia and New Zealanc

26 *Friday*   Boxing Day (St Stephen's Day)
                                        Holiday, UK, Republic of Ireland, Canada
                                                      Australia and New Zealand

27 *Saturday*

28 *Sunday*   *First Quarter*

European Robin (*Erithacus rubecula*) adult, perched on European Holly (*Ilex aquifolium*)

DECEMBER AND JANUARY 2015

Monday 29

Tuesday 30

New Year's Eve

Wednesday 31

New Year's Day
Holiday, UK, Republic of Ireland, USA, Canada,
Australia and New Zealand

Thursday 1

Holiday, Scotland and New Zealand

Friday 2

Saturday 3

Sunday 4

Blue Tit (*Parus caeruleus*) adults, flock feeding

NOTES